The

WANNABOO

W9-BNT-296

Alf and Frank slept in the
tent in the camp.
Alf and Frank slept well.

But the smell ...
The smell is a stink!
Alf and Frank smelt the stink.

Alf sniffs. Frank sniffs.

Is the stink from the pond?

The smell is not from the pond.

The stink is from the stump.
Frank and Alf crept up to
the stump.

It is Punk, the skunk!
The stink is from Punk!

Frank and Alf dunk Punk in the pond.

Game page

On the next page is a game for two to help you practise reading the words in this book.

Photocopy the page twice and cut up one page to make word cards.

Cut the other page in half to make two base cards. Place the word cards face down on the table.

Take turns to pick up a card.

Read the word aloud.

Place the matching word card on your base card. If you do not have the word on your base card, put it back face down with the other cards.

The winner is the first one to fill their base card!

City of
Wanneroo
Libraries

The stink

AL11003573761B